Grade 6

The Syllabus of Examinations should be read for details of requirements, especially those for scales, aural tests and sight-reading. Attention should be paid to the Special Notices on the front inside cover, where warning is given of changes.

The syllabus is obtainable from music dealers or from The Associated Board of the Royal Schools of Music, 14 Bedford Square, London WC1B 3JG (please send stamped addressed envelope measuring about 9×6 ins.).

In overseas centres, information may be obtained from the Local Representative or Resident Secretary.

REQUIREMENTS

SCALES AND ARPEGGIOS (from memory)

Scales
in similar motion with hands together one octave apart, in all keys, major and minor, both melodic and harmonic (four octaves);
and in contrary motion, hands beginning and ending on the key-note (unison), in the keys specified in one of the following groups chosen by the candidate (two octaves):
Group 1 – D♭, F, A majors:
Group 2 – D, F♯, B♭ majors.

Chromatic Scales
hands together in similar motion one octave apart, beginning on any note named by the examiner (four octaves);
and in contrary motion, beginning on C with the left hand and E with the right, a third apart (two octaves).

Arpeggios
with hands together one octave apart:
major and minor common chords, root position only, in all keys (four octaves);
diminished seventh chords, beginning on B, C & C♯ (three octaves).

PLAYING AT SIGHT

AURAL TESTS (see current syllabus)

THREE PIECES

Candidates should choose one piece from Group A, one piece from Group B, and the third piece *either* from Group C *or* from the further alternatives listed below:

Albéniz Zortzico, Op.165 No.6
Skryabin Prelude in G minor, Op.11 No.22
These are included in More Romantic Pieces for Piano, Book IV, *published by the Associated Board*

Editor for the Associated Board: **Lionel Salter**

Printed in England

Other pieces have been checked with original source material and edited as necessary for instructional purposes. Fingering, phrasing, pedalling, metronome marks and the editorial realization of ornaments (where given) are for guidance but are not comprehensive or obligatory. Any good alternatives, which are appropriate in style, will be accepted by the examiners.

A:1

ALLEMANDE in A

Edited by
Richard Jones

HANDEL, HWV 477

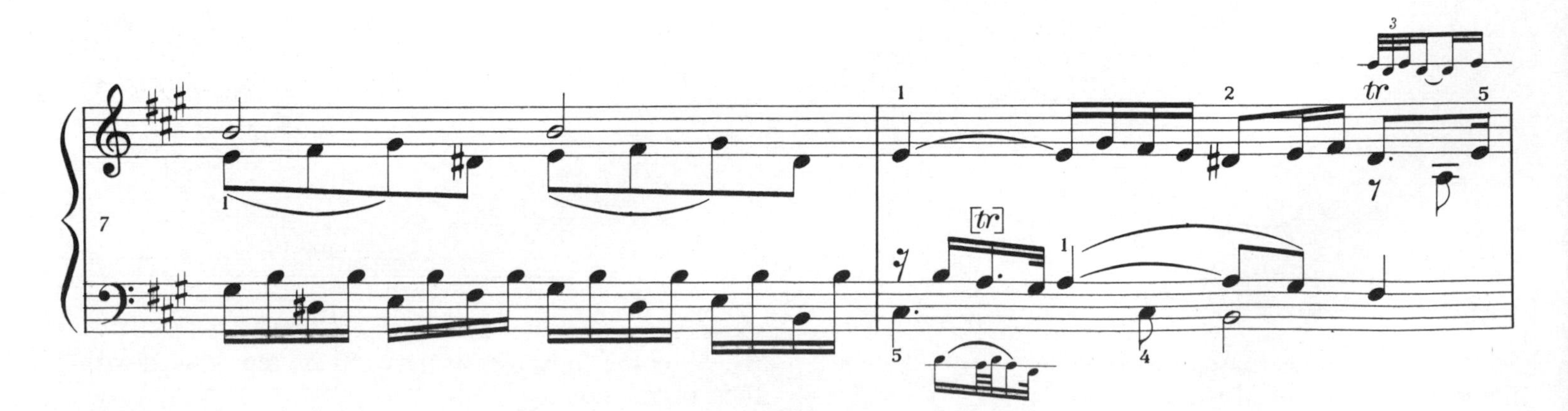

Source: autograph copy in the Fitzwilliam Museum, Cambridge. All slurs are editorial, as are trills within square brackets.

Reprinted from Händel, *Selected Keyboard Works*, Book I, edited by Richard Jones (Associated Board)

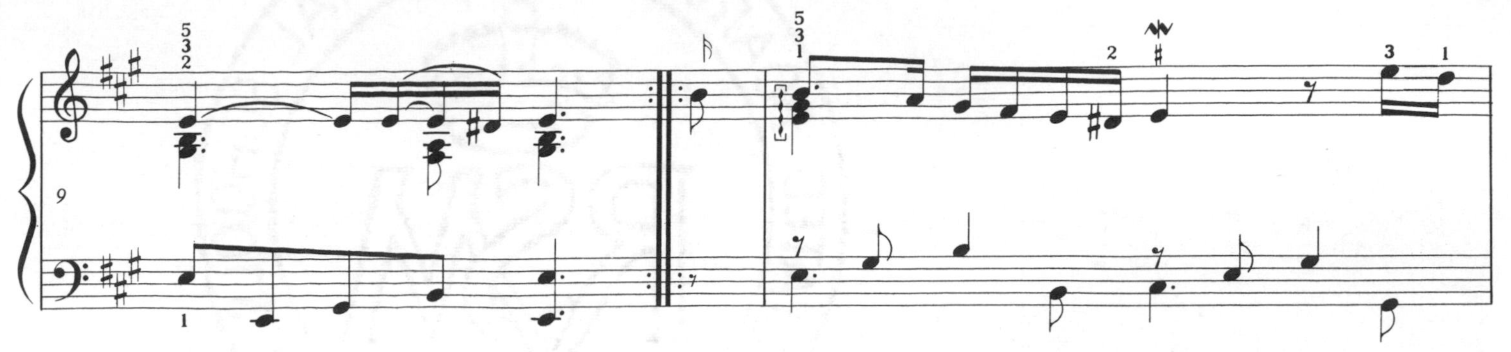

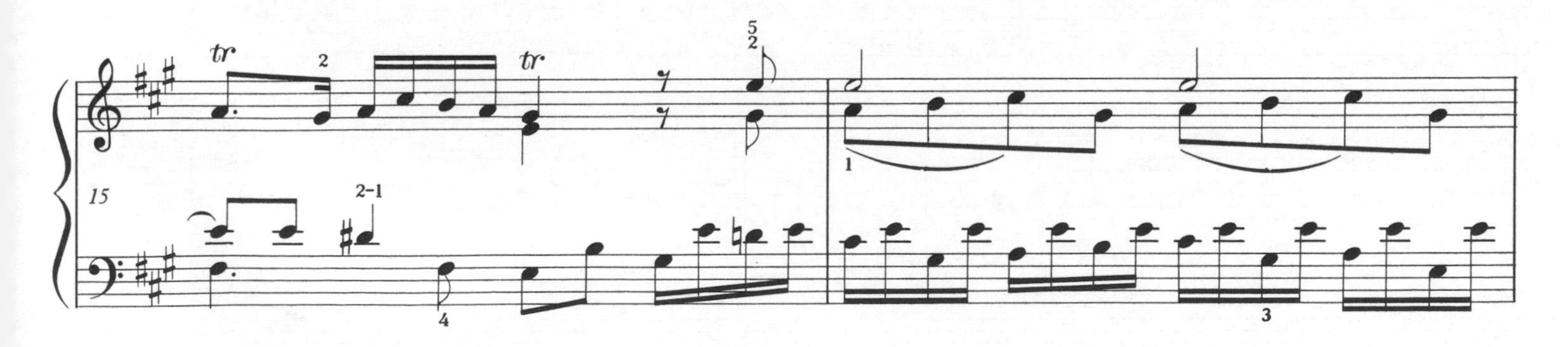

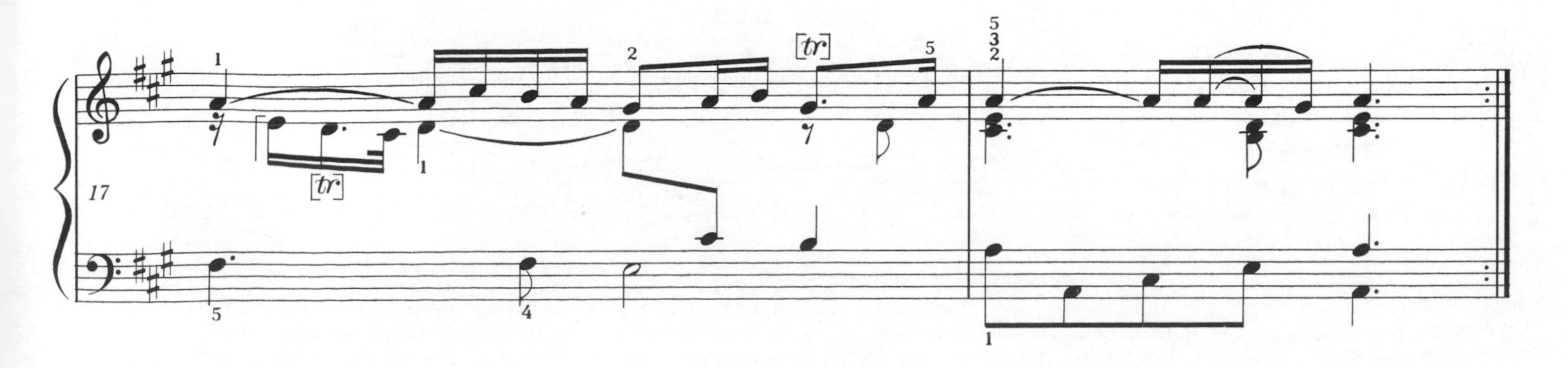

A:2
SONATA in D
First movement

GALUPPI, Op.1 No.4

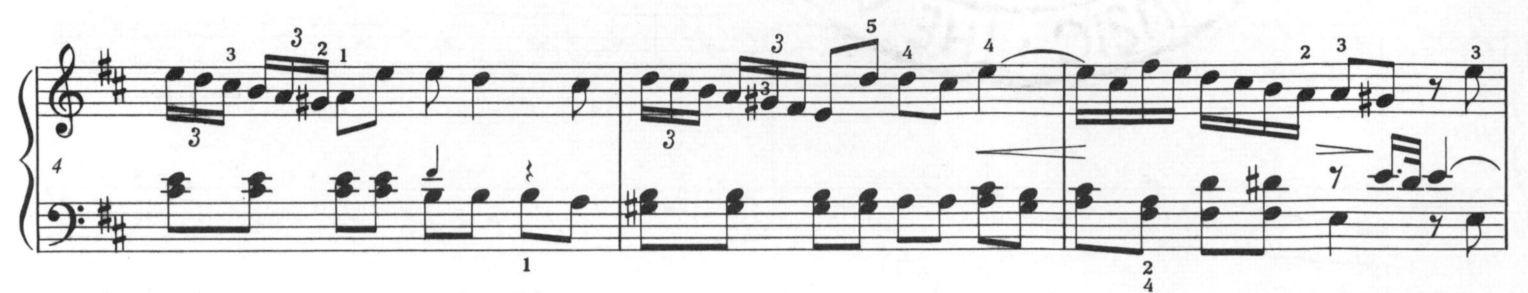

Source: Galuppi's *Sonate per cembalo* (Op.1); London, 1750. The thematic catalogue by Hedda Illy of Galuppi's keyboard music disregards the order of Op.1 and Op.2 sonatas as printed by Walsh in London, and lists the present sonata as No.45, but in the key of E. Dynamics are by the present editor, who has written out appoggiaturas and also corrected some obvious errors. Trills should begin on the upper note, and in the case of dotted quavers should preferably end on the dot. L.S.

B:1
SONATA in D
Third movement

HAYDN, Hob.XVI/24

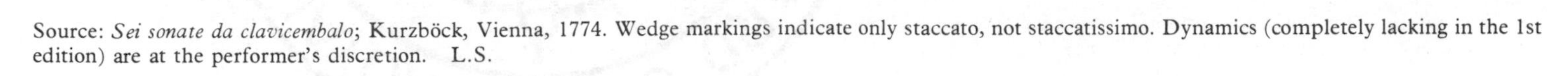
Source: *Sei sonate da clavicembalo*; Kurzböck, Vienna, 1774. Wedge markings indicate only staccato, not staccatissimo. Dynamics (completely lacking in the 1st edition) are at the performer's discretion. L.S.

75

81

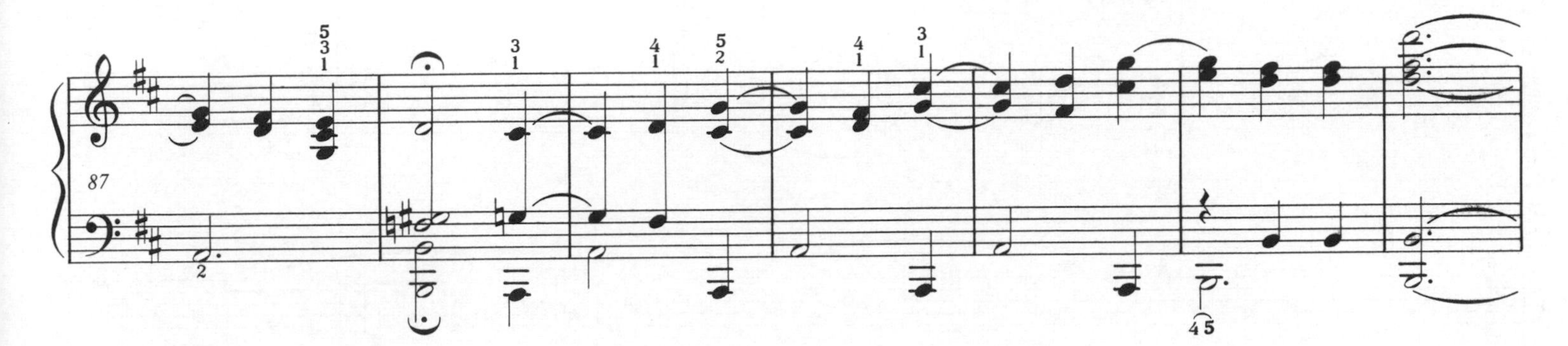
87

94

100

106

B:2

ALLEGRETTO in C minor

Edited by
Howard Ferguson

SCHUBERT, D.915

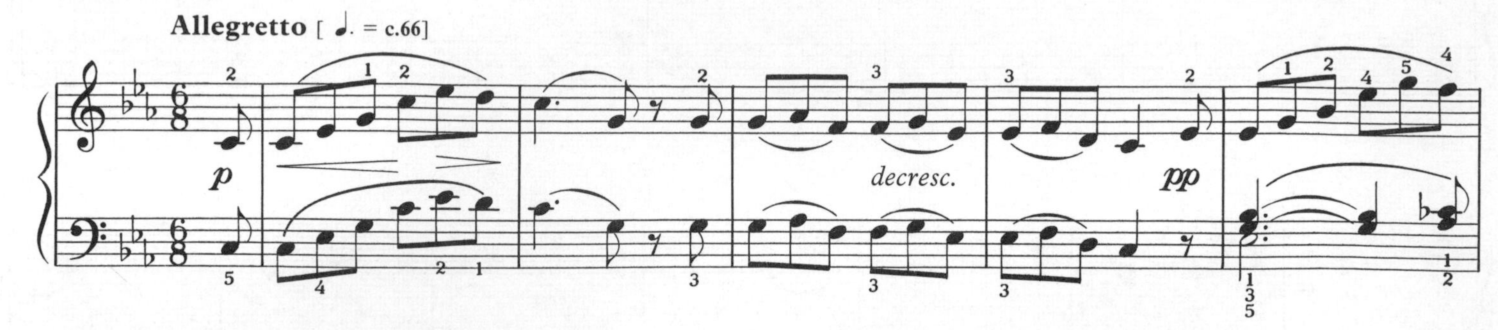

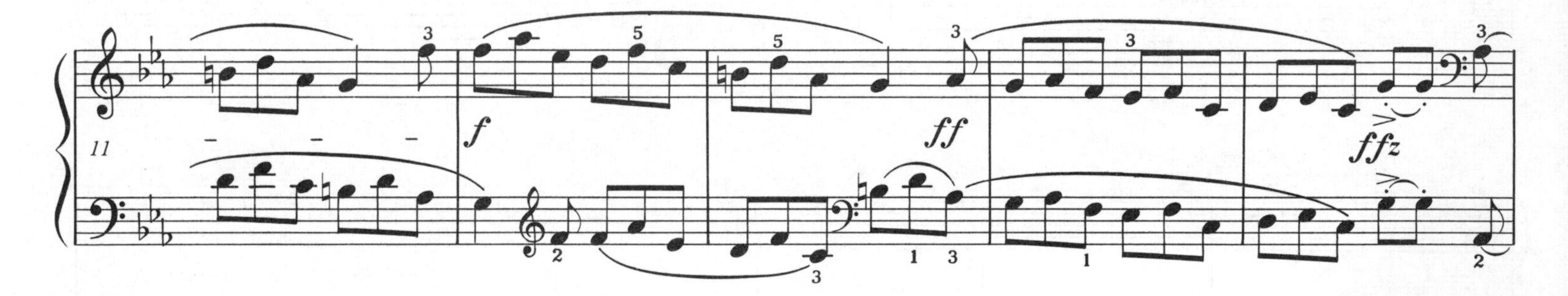

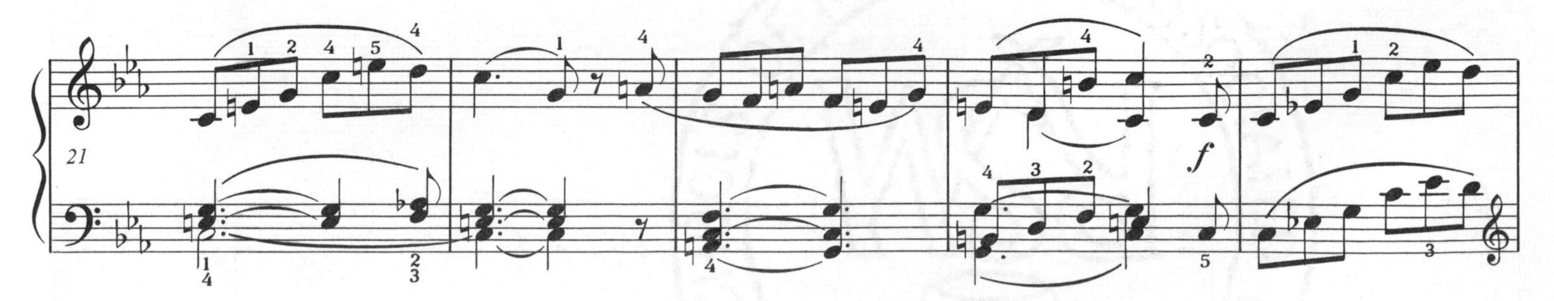

Source: 1st edition, *Allegretto für Pianoforte . . . (Nachgelassenes Werk)*; J.P. Gotthard, Vienna, 1870. This piece originated in the autograph album of Ferdinand Walcher, a lawyer and amateur singer. In bar 32 there were no naturals to the R.H. notes B: the slurs in bars 33 and 49, and the dynamic in bar 8, are editorial.

Reprinted from Schubert, *Nine Short Piano Pieces*, edited by Howard Ferguson (Associated Board)

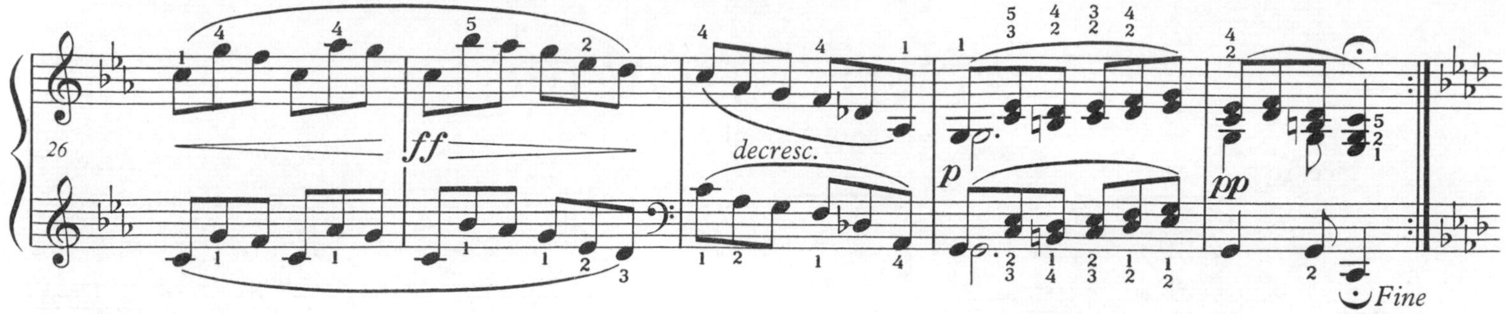
26
ff
decresc.
p
pp
Fine

31 pp

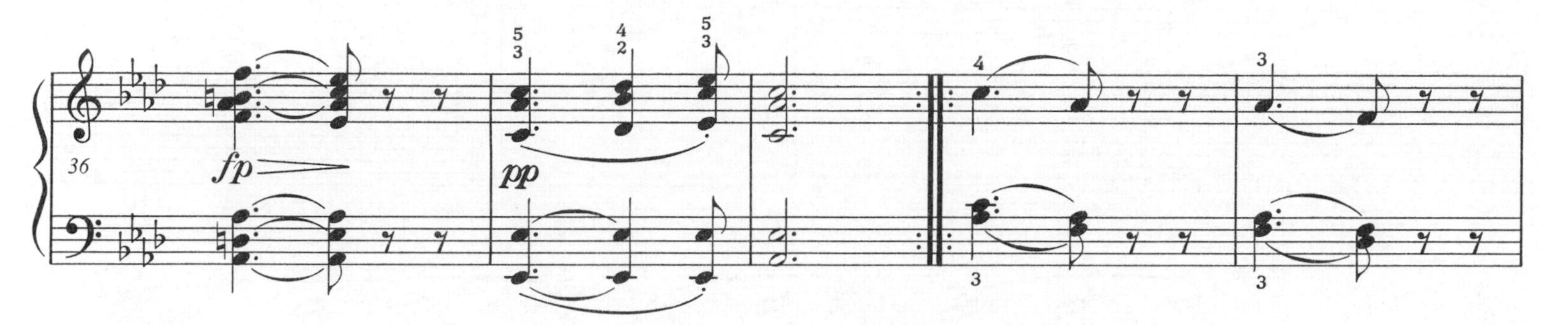
36
fp
pp

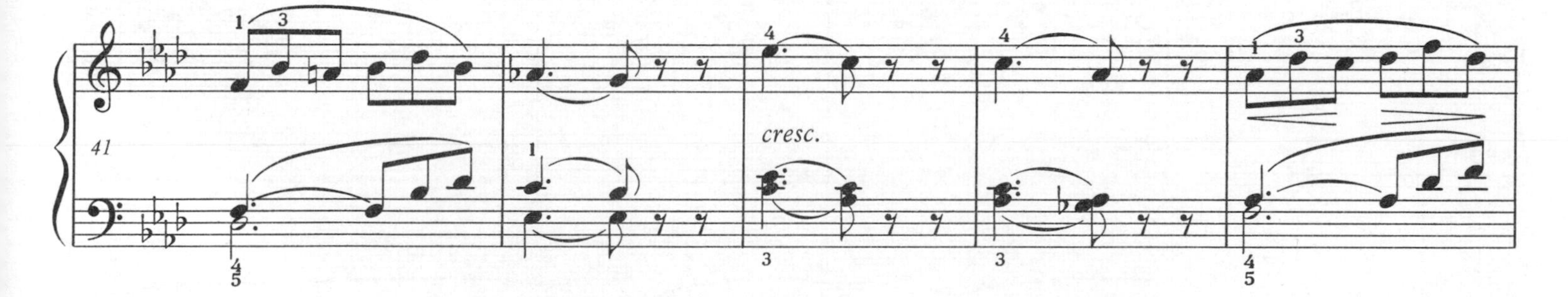
41
cresc.

46
pp

52
f
pp
pp
D.C. al Fine

C:1
APRIL SHOWER
from 'April Morn'

Presto [♪ = 200]

ALWYN

21
dim.
mp

25
cresc.
dim.

Tempo I
rall.
29
dolce
pp
P

33
P

senza rit.
37
dim.
ppp
P
sec

C:2
COLUMBINE DANCES
from 'Puppets', Book I

MARTINŮ

Tempo di Valse (𝅗𝅥. = c.56)

Poco vivo

19 *f*

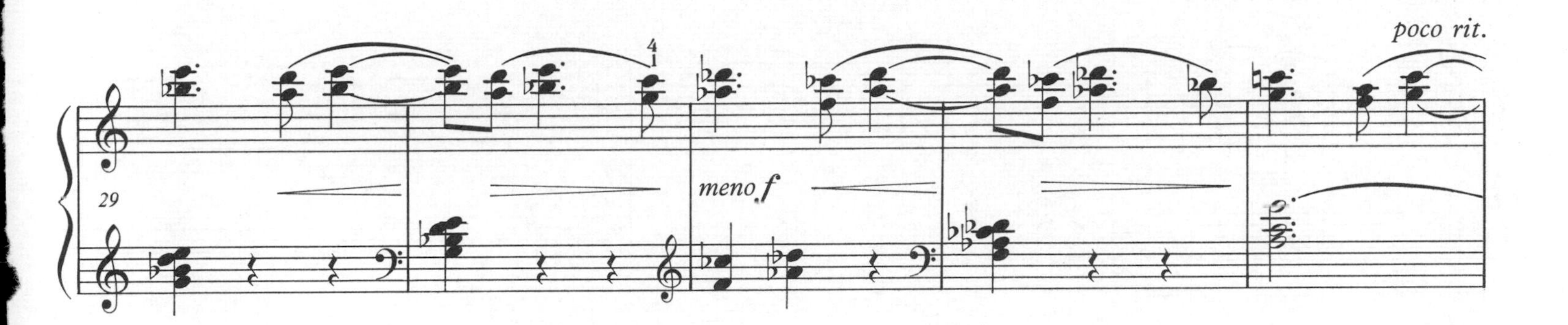

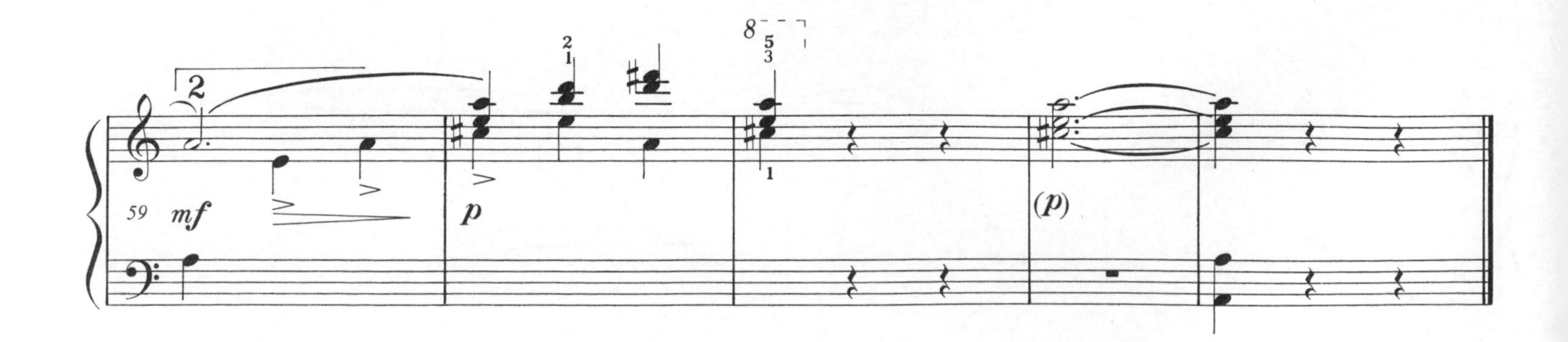

Printed in Great Britain by Headley Brothers Ltd The Invicta Press Ashford Kent and London 2/92